THE CHRISTMAS
CHRISTMAS
CAROLING SONGBOOK

MELODY, WORDS AND CHORDS FOR 72 FAVORITE CAROLS AND SONGS

W9-BAS-755

ISBN 978-1-4803-4533-1

HAL•LEONARD®
CORPORATION

7777 W. BLUEMOUND RD. P.O. BOX 13819 MILWAUKEE, WI 53213

Visit Hal Leonard Online at
www.halleonard.com

ALL THROUGH THE NIGHT

Welsh Folksong

Moderately

Sleep, my Child, and peace at-tend Thee, all through the
While the moon, her watch is keep-ing, all through the
You, my God, a Babe of won-der, all through the

night; Guard-ian an-gels God will send Thee,
night; While the wea-ry world is sleep-ing,
night; Dreams you dream can't break from thun-der,

all through the night; Soft the drows-y
all through the night; Through your dreams you're
all through the night; Chil-dren's dreams can-

hours are creep-ing, Hill and vale in slum-ber sleep-ing,
swift-ly steal-ing, Vi-sions of de-light re-veal-ing.
not be bro-ken; Life is but a love-ly to-ken.

God His lov-ing vig-il keep-ing, all through the night.
Christ-mas time is so ap-peal-ing, all through the night.
Christ-mas should be soft-ly spo-ken, all through the night.

ANGELS WE HAVE HEARD ON HIGH

Traditional French Carol
Translated by JAMES CHADWICK

AS WITH GLADNESS MEN OF OLD

Words by WILLIAM CHATTERTON DIX
Music by CONRAD KOCHER

AULD LANG SYNE

Words by ROBERT BURNS
Traditional Scottish Melody

Should auld ac-quaint-ance be for-got, and nev-er brought to mind? Should

auld ac-quaint-ance be for-got and days of auld lang syne? For

auld ___ lang ___ syne, my dear, for auld ___ lang ___ syne, We'll

tak' a cup o' kind - ness yet, for ___ auld ___ lang ___ syne.

AWAY IN A MANGER

Traditional
Words by JOHN T. McFARLAND (v. 3)
Music by JAMES R. MURRAY

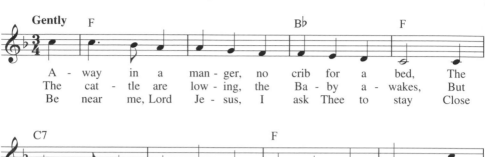

A - way in a man - ger, no crib for a bed, The
The cat - tle are low - ing, the Ba - by a - wakes, But
Be near me, Lord Je - sus, I ask Thee to stay Close

lit - tle Lord Je - sus laid down His sweet head. The
lit tle Lord Je - sus no cry - ing He makes. I
by me for - ev - er, and love me, I pray. Bless

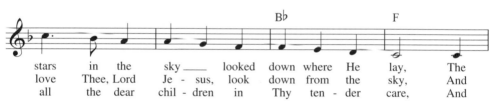

stars in the sky ___ looked down where He lay, The
love Thee, Lord Je - sus, look down from the sky, And
all the dear chil - dren in Thy ten - der care, And

lit - tle Lord Je - sus, a - sleep on the hay.
stay by my cra - dle till morn - ing is nigh.
fit us for heav - en to live with Thee there.

BLUE CHRISTMAS

Words and Music by BILLY HAYES
and JAY JOHNSON

With expression

I'll have a blue Christ-mas with - out you. _____ I'll be so

blue think-ing a - bout you. _____ Dec - o - ra - tions of

red on a green Christ-mas tree won't mean a thing if

you're not here with me. I'll have a blue Christ-mas, that's

cer - tain. _____ And when that blue heart-ache starts hurt - in', _____

_____ you'll be do - in' all right, with your Christ - mas of

white, but I'll have a blue, blue Christ-mas. _____

CAROL OF THE BELLS

Ukrainian Christmas Carol

Exuberantly

Hark to the bells, hark to the bells, tell - ing us all Je - sus is King!

Strong - ly they chime, sound with a rhyme, Christ-mas is here, wel - come the King!

Hark to the bells, hark to the bells, this is the day, day of the King!

Peal out the news o'er hill and dale, and 'round the town tell - ing the tale.

Hark to the bells, hark to the bells, tell - ing us all Je - sus is King!

Come, one and all____ hap - pi - ly sing____ Songs of good will ____

O let them sing! Ring, _____ sil - v'ry bells,

Sing, _____ joy - ous bells! Strong-ly they chime, sound with a rhyme,

Christ-mas is here, wel-come the King! Hark to the bells, hark to the bells,

tell - ing us all Je - sus is King! Ring! Ring! _ bells. ____

CAROLING, CAROLING

Words by WIHLA HUTSON
Music by ALFRED BURT

With a lilt

Car - ol - ing, car - ol - ing, now we go; Christ - mas bells are
Car - ol - ing, car - ol - ing, thru the town; Christ - mas bells are

ring - ing! Car - ol - ing, car - ol - ing, thru the snow;
ring - ing! Car - ol - ing, car - ol - ing, up and down;

Christ - mas bells are ring - ing! Joy - ous voic - es
Christ - mas bells are ring - ing! Mark ye well the

sweet and clear, Sing the sad of heart to cheer.
song we sing, Glad - some tid - ings now we bring.

Ding, dong, ding, dong, Christ - mas bells are ring - ing!
Ding, dong, ding, dong, Christ - mas bells are ring - ing!

CHRIST WAS BORN ON CHRISTMAS DAY

Traditional

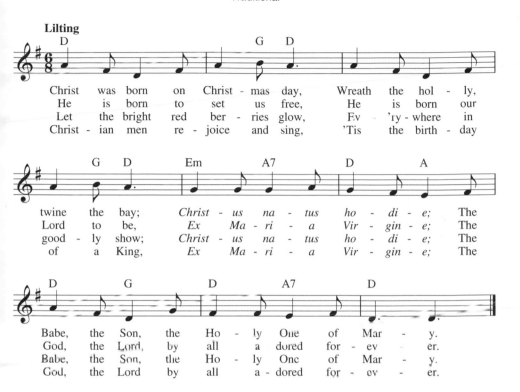

Lilting

D   G   D

Christ was born on Christ - mas day,   Wreath the hol - ly,
He is born to set us free,   He is born our
Let the bright red ber - ries glow,   Ev 'ry - where in
Christ - ian men re - joice and sing,   'Tis the birth - day

G   D   Em   A7   D   A

twine the bay;   *Christ - us na - tus*   *ho - di - e;*   The
Lord to be,   *Ex Ma - ri - a*   *Vir - gin - e;*   The
good - ly show;   *Christ - us na - tus*   *ho - di - e;*   The
of a King,   *Ex Ma - ri - a*   *Vir - gin - e;*   The

D   G   D   A7   D

Babe, the Son, the Ho - ly One of Mar - y.
God, the Lord, by all a dored for - ev - er.
Babe, the Son, the Ho - ly One of Mar - y.
God, the Lord by all a - dored for - ev - er.

CHRISTMAS IS A-COMIN'
(May God Bless You)

Words and Music by
FRANK LUTHER

Moderately slow

When I'm feel - in' blue, An' when I'm feel - in' low,

Then I start to think a - bout the hap - pi - est man I know; He

does - n't mind the snow An' he does - n't mind the rain, But

all De - cem - ber you will hear him at your win - dow - pane, a -

sing in' a - gain an' a - gain an' a - gain an' a - gain an' a - gain an' a - gain.

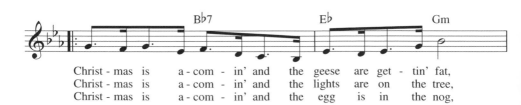

Christ - mas is a - com - in' and the geese are get - tin' fat,
Christ - mas is a - com - in' and the lights are on the tree,
Christ - mas is a - com - in' and the egg is in the nog,

15

Please to put a pen - ny in a poor man's hat. If you
How a - bout a tur - key leg for poor old me? If you
Please to let me sit a-round your old yule log. If you'd

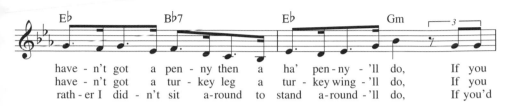

have - n't got a pen - ny then a ha' pen-ny-'ll do, If you
have - n't got a tur - key leg a tur - key wing-'ll do, If you
rath - er I did - n't sit a-round to stand a-round-'ll do, If you'd

have - n't got a ha' pen - ny, may God bless you.
have - n't got a tur - key wing, may God bless you.
rath - er I did - n't stand a - round, may God bless you.

God bless you, gen - tle - men, God bless you, If you
God bless you, gen - tle - men, God bless you, If you
God bless you, gen - tle - men, God bless you, If you'd

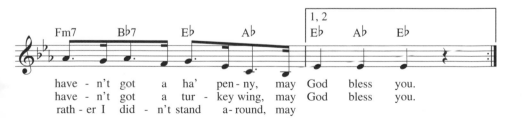

have - n't got a ha' pen - ny, may God bless you.
have - n't got a tur - key wing, may God bless you.
rath - er I did - n't stand a - round, may

God bless you, If you have-n't got a thing for me, may God bless you.

THE CHRISTMAS SONG
(Chestnuts Roasting on an Open Fire)

Music and Lyric by MEL TORME
and ROBERT WELLS

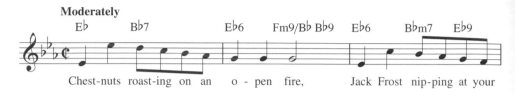

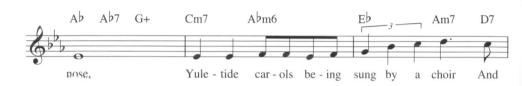

Chest-nuts roast-ing on an o - pen fire, Jack Frost nip-ping at your

nose, Yule - tide car - ols be - ing sung by a choir And

folks dressed up like Es - ki - mos, Ev-'ry-bod-y knows a tur-key and some

mis - tle - toe ____ Help to make the sea-son bright.

Ti - ny tots with their eyes all a - glow Will find it hard to sleep to -

night. They know that San - ta's on his way; He's load-ed

lots of toys and good-ies on his sleigh, And ev-'ry moth-er's child _ is gon-na spy _____ To see if rein-deer _ real-ly know how to fly.

And so, I'm of-fer-ing this sim-ple phrase To kids from one to nine-ty - two. Al-tho' it's been said man-y times, man - y ways; "Mer - ry Christ - mas to you."

CHRISTMAS TIME IS HERE

from A CHARLIE BROWN CHRISTMAS™
Words by LEE MENDELSON
Music by VINCE GUARALDI

Slowly

Christ-mas time is here, hap-pi-ness and cheer, fun for all, that chil-dren call their fa-v'rite time of year.

Snow-flakes in the air, car-ols ev-'ry-where, old-en times and an-cient rhymes of love, and dreams to share.

Sleigh-bells in the air, beau-ty ev-'ry-where, Yule-tide by the fire-side, and joy-ful mem-'ries there.

Christ-mas time is here, fam-'lies draw-ing near, oh, that we could al-ways see such spir-it through the years.

THE COVENTRY CAROL

Words by ROBERT CROO
Traditional English Melody

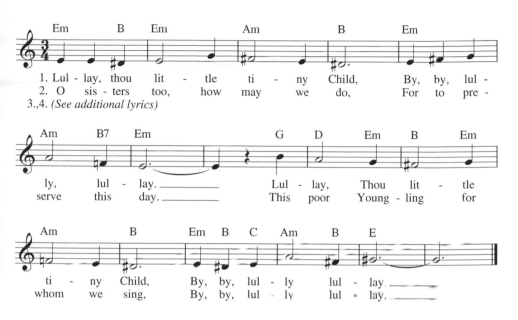

1. Lul - lay, thou lit - tle ti - ny Child, By, by, lul -
2. O sis - ters too, how may we do, For to pre -
3.,4. *(See additional lyrics)*

ly, lul - lay. _____ Lul - lay, Thou lit - tle
serve this day. _____ This poor Young - ling for

ti - ny Child, By, by, lul - ly lul - lay. _____
whom we sing, By, by, lul - ly lul - lay. _____

Additional lyrics

3. Herod, the King
In his raging,
Charged he hath this day.
His men of might,
In his own sight,
All young children to slay.

4. That woe is me,
Poor child for thee!
And ever morn and day,
For thy parting
Neither say nor sing
By, by, lully, lullay.

DECK THE HALL

Traditional Welsh Carol

Brightly

1. Deck the hall with boughs of hol - ly, Fa la la la la, la
'Tis the sea - son to be jol - ly, Fa la la la la, la
2.,3. *(See additional lyrics)*

la la la.
la la la. Don we now our gay ap - par - rel,

Fa la la la la la la, Troll the an - cient

Yule - tide car - ol, Fa la la la la, la la la la.

Additional Lyrics

2. See the blazing Yule before us, Fa la la la la, la la la la.
Strike the harp and join the chorus, Fa la la la la, la la la la.
Follow me in merry measure, Fa la la la la la la.
While I tell of Yuletide treasure, Fa la la la la, la la la la.

3. Fast away the old year passes, Fa la la la la, la la la la.
Hail the new, ye lads and lasses, Fa la la la la, la la la la.
Sing we joyous all together, Fa la la la la la la.
Heedless of the wind and weather, Fa la la la la, la la la la.

DING DONG! MERRILY ON HIGH!

French Carol

Additional Lyrics

3. Pray you, dutifully prime your matin chime, ye ringers;
   May you beautifully rime your evetime song, ye singers.

DO YOU HEAR WHAT I HEAR

Words and Music by NOEL REGNEY
and GLORIA SHAYNE

Moderately, with feeling

Said the night wind to the lit-tle lamb,
lit-tle lamb to the shep-herd boy,
shep-herd boy to the might-y king,
king to the peo-ple ev-'ry-where,

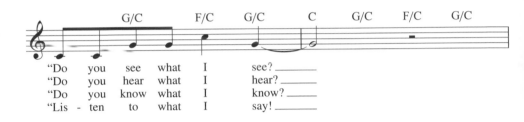

"Do you see what I see? _____
"Do you hear what I hear? _____
"Do you know what I know? _____
"Lis-ten to what I say! _____

Way up in the sky, lit-tle lamb,
Ring-ing through the sky, shep-herd boy,
In your pal-ace warm, might-y king,
Pray for peace, ___ peo-ple ev-'ry-where,

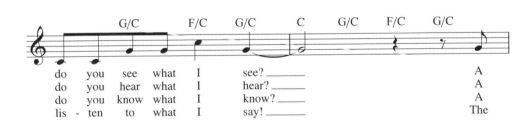

do you see what I see? _____ A
do you hear what I hear? _____ A
do you know what I know? _____ A
lis-ten to what I say! _____ The

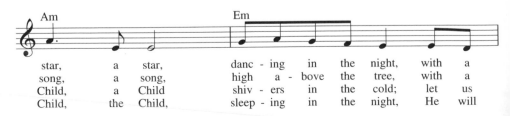

star, a star, danc-ing in the night, with a
song, a song, high a-bove the tree, with a
Child, a Child shiv-ers in the cold; let us
Child, the Child, sleep-ing in the night, He will

23

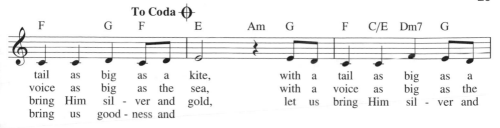

To Coda ⊕

F   G F   E   Am G   F C/E Dm7 G

tail as big as a kite, with a tail as big as a
voice as big as the sea, with a voice as big as the
bring Him sil - ver and gold, let us bring Him sil - ver and
bring us good - ness and

C   Gm7   **1, 2** C   **3** C   **D.S. al Coda**

kite." Said the
sea." Said the
gold." Said the

CODA ⊕ E Am G   F C/E   Dm7 Em/G   G7

opt.

light, He will bring us good - ness and

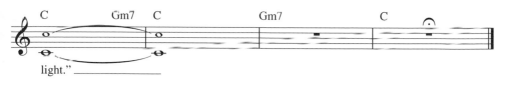

C Gm7 C   Gm7   C

light." _____

FELIZ NAVIDAD

Music and Lyrics by
JOSÉ FELICIANO

THE FIRST NOEL

17th Century English Carol
Music from W. Sandys' *Christmas Carols*

THE FRIENDLY BEASTS

Traditional English Carol

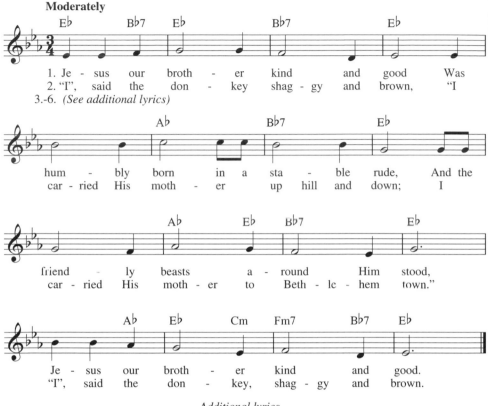

Moderately

1. Je - sus our broth - er kind and good Was
2. "I", said the don - key shag - gy and brown, "I
3.-6. *(See additional lyrics)*

hum - bly born in a sta - ble rude, And the
car - ried His moth - er up hill and down; I

friend - ly beasts a - round Him stood,
car - ried His moth - er to Beth - le - hem town."

Je - sus our broth - er kind and good.
"I", said the don - key, shag - gy and brown.

Additional lyrics

3. "I," said the cow all white and red,
"I gave Him my manger for His bed;
I gave Him my hay to pillow His head."
"I," said the cow all white and red.

4. "I," said the sheep with the curly horn,
"I gave Him my wool for His blanket warm;
He wore my coat on Christmas morn."
"I," said the sheep with the curly horn.

5. "I," said the dove from the rafters high,
"I cooed Him to sleep that He would not cry;
We cooed Him to sleep, my mate and I."
"I," said the dove from the rafters high.

6. Thus every beast by some good spell,
In the stable dark was glad to tell
Of the gift he gave Emmanuel,
The gift he gave Emmanuel.

FROM HEAVEN ABOVE TO EARTH I COME

Words and Music by
MARTIN LUTHER

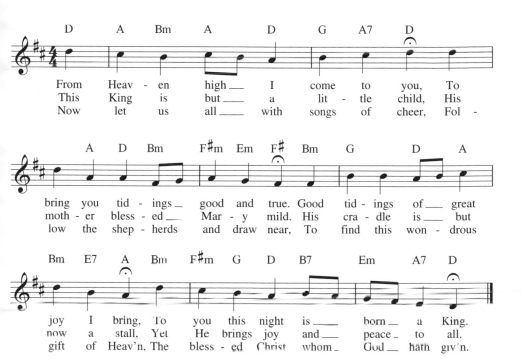

From Heav - en high __ I come to you, To
This King is but __ a lit - tle child, His
Now let us all __ with songs of cheer, Fol -

bring you tid - ings __ good and true. Good tid - ings of __ great
moth - er bless - ed __ Mar - y mild. His cra - dle is __ but
low the shep - herds and draw near, To find this won - drous

joy I bring, To you this night is __ born __ a King.
now a stall, Yet He brings joy and __ peace _ to all.
gift of Heav'n, The bless - ed Christ whom _ God __ hath giv'n.

FROSTY THE SNOW MAN

Words and Music by STEVE NELSON
and JACK ROLLINS

Moderately

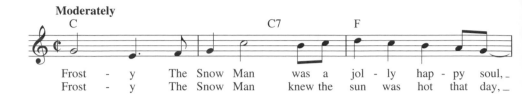

Frost - y The Snow Man was a jol - ly hap - py soul, _
Frost - y The Snow Man knew the sun was hot that day, _

___ With a corn - cob pipe and a but - ton nose _ and two
___ So he said, "Let's run and we'll have some fun _ now be -

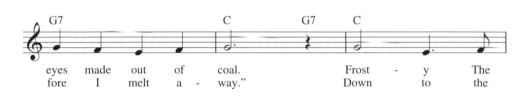

eyes made out of coal. Frost - y The
fore I melt a - way." Down to the

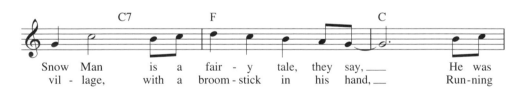

Snow Man is a fair - y tale, they say, ___ He was
vil - lage, with a broom - stick in his hand, ___ Run - ning

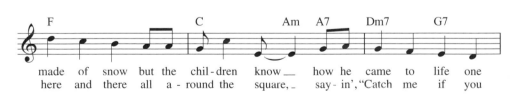

made of snow but the chil - dren know _ how he came to life one
here and there all a - round the square, _ say - in', "Catch me if you

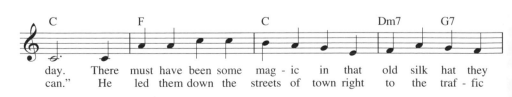

day. There must have been some mag - ic in that old silk hat they
can." He led them down the streets of town right to the traf - fic

found. For when they placed it on his head he be -
cop. And he on - ly paused a mo - ment when __ he

gan to dance a - round. Oh, Frost - y The
heard him hol - ler, "Stop!" For Frost - y The

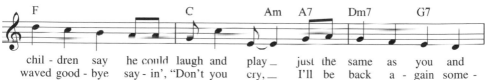

Snow Man was a - live as he could be, __ And the
Snow Man had to hur - ry on his way, __ But he

chil - dren say he could laugh and play __ just the same as you and
waved good - bye say - in', "Don't you cry, __ I'll be back a - gain some -

me. Thump-et - y thump thump, thump-et - y thump thump.
day."

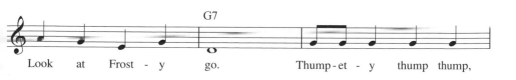

Look at Frost - y go. Thump - et - y thump thump,

thump-et - y thump thump. O - ver the hills of snow.

FUM, FUM, FUM

Traditional Catalonian Carol

GO, TELL IT ON THE MOUNTAIN

African-American Spiritual
Verses by JOHN W. WORK, JR.

GOD REST YE MERRY, GENTLEMEN

19th Century English Carol

GOOD CHRISTIAN MEN, REJOICE

14th Century Latin Text
Translated by JOHN MASON NEALE
14th Century German Melody

GOOD KING WENCESLAS

Words by JOHN M. NEALE
Music from *Piae Cantiones*

1. Good King Wen - ces - las looked out On the feast of Ste - phen, When the snow lay 'round a - bout, Deep, and crisp, and e - ven; Bright - ly shone the moon that night, Though the frost was cru - el, When a poor man came in sight, Gath-'ring win - ter fu - el.

2. "Hith - er, page, and stand by me, If thou know'st it, tell - ing, Yon - der pea - sant, who is he? Where and what his dwell - ing?" "Sire, he lives a good league hence, Un - der - neath the moun - tain, Right a - gainst the for - est fence, By Saint Ag - nes' foun - tain."

3.-5. *(See additional lyrics)*

Additional Lyrics

3. "Bring me flesh, and bring me wine,
   bring me pine-logs hither;
Thou and I will see him dine,
   when we bear them thither."
Page and monarch, forth they went,
   forth they went together;
Through the rude wind's wild lament
   and the bitter weather.

4. "Sire, the night is darker now,
   and the wind blows stronger;
Fails me heart, I know not how;
   I can go no longer."
"Mark my footsteps, good my page;
   tread thou in them boldly;
Thou shalt find the winter's rage
   freeze thy blood less coldly."

5. In his master's steps he trod,
   where the snow lay dinted;
Heat was in the very sod
   which the saint had printed.
Therefore, Christian men, be sure,
   wealth or rank possessing,
Ye who now will bless the poor,
   shall yourselves find blessing.

HAPPY HOLIDAY

from the Motion Picture Irving Berlin's HOLIDAY INN
Words and Music by
IRVING BERLIN

HARK! THE HERALD ANGELS SING

Words by CHARLES WESLEY
Altered by GEORGE WHITEFIELD
Music by FELIX MENDELSSOHN-BARTHOLDY
Arranged by William H. Cummings

HERE COMES SANTA CLAUS
(Right Down Santa Claus Lane)
Words and Music by GENE AUTRY
and OAKLEY HALDEMAN

HERE WE COME A-WASSAILING

Traditional

Here we come a-was-sail-ing A-mong the leaves so green; Here we come a wan-d'ring so fair___ to be seen; Love and joy come to you, And to you your was-sail too; And God bless you, and send___ you a Hap-py New Year, And God send you a Hap-py New Year.___

THE HOLLY AND THE IVY

18th Century English Carol

1.,6. The hol-ly and the i - vy, when they are both full grown, of __
2. The hol-ly bears a blos - som, as white as lil - y flow'r, and __
3. The hol-ly bears a ber - ry, as red as an - y blood, and __
4. The hol-ly bears a prick - le, as sharp as an - y thorn, and __
5. The hol-ly bears a bark, __ as bit-ter as an-y gall, and __

Refrain

all the trees that are in the wood, the __ hol - ly bears the crown.
Mar-y bore sweet _ Je - sus Christ, to __ be our sweet Sav - iour.
Mar-y bore sweet _ Je - sus Christ, to __ do poor sin - ners good.
Mar-y bore sweet _ Je - sus Christ on _ Christ-mas day in the morn.
Mar-y bore sweet _ Je - sus Christ for __ to re-deem us all.

The

ris-ing of the sun __ and the run-ning of the deer, the __

play-ing of the mer - ry or - gan, sweet sing-ing in the choir.

A HOLLY JOLLY CHRISTMAS

Music and Lyrics by
JOHNNY MARKS

I HEARD THE BELLS ON CHRISTMAS DAY

Words by HENRY WADSWORTH LONGFELLOW
Adapted by JOHNNY MARKS
Music by JOHNNY MARKS

(There's No Place Like)
HOME FOR THE HOLIDAYS
Words by AL STILLMAN
Music by ROBERT ALLEN

Oh, there's no place like home for the hol-i-days; ___ 'Cause no

mat-ter how far a-way you roam, ___ When you

pine for the sun-shine of a friend-ly gaze, ___ for the

hol-i-days you can't beat home, sweet home. I met a

man who lives in Ten-nes-see and he was head-in' for Penn-syl-

va-nia and some home-made pump-kin pie. From Penn-syl-

va - nia folks are trav - 'lin' down to Dix - ie's sun - ny shores; From At -

lan - tic to Pa - cif - ic, gee, the traf - fic is ter - rif - ic. Oh, there's

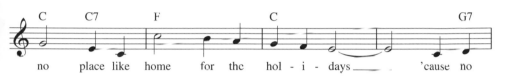

no place like home for the hol - i - days _____ 'cause no

mat - ter how far a - way you roam, _____ If you

want to be hap - py in a mil - lion ways _____ For the

hol - i - days you can't beat home, sweet home. _____ Oh, there's

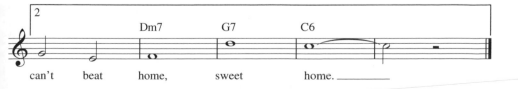

can't beat home, sweet home. _____

I SAW MOMMY KISSING SANTA CLAUS

Words and Music by
TOMMIE CONNOR

I WONDER AS I WANDER

By JOHN JACOB NILES

1.,4. I won-der as I wan-der out un-der the sky, how
2. Mar-y birthed Je-sus, 'twas in a cow's stall, with
3. Je-sus had want-ed for an-y wee thing, a

Je-sus the Sav-ior did come for to die for
wise men and farm-ers and shep-herds and all. But
star in the sky or a bird on the wing, or

poor on-'ry peo-ple like you and like I... I
high from God's heav-en a star's light did fall, and the
all of God's an-gels in heav'n for to sing, He

won-der as I wan-der out un-der the sky. When
prom-ise of ag-es it then did re-call. If
sure-ly could have it, 'cause He was the King. I

un-der the sky.

I'LL BE HOME FOR CHRISTMAS

Words and Music by KIM GANNON
and WALTER KENT

IT CAME UPON THE MIDNIGHT CLEAR

Words by EDMUND HAMILTON SEARS
Music by RICHARD STORRS WILLIS

IT MUST HAVE BEEN THE MISTLETOE
(Our First Christmas)
By JUSTIN WILDE
and DOUG KONECKY

Moderately

F(add9)

It must have been the mis-tle-toe, ___ the
could have been the hol-i-day, ___ the
must have been the mis-tle-toe, ___ the

F(add9)/A   Bb(add9)

la zy fire, _ the fall-ing snow, _ the mag-ic in __ the frost-y air, ___ that
mid-night ride _ up-on a sleigh, _ thc coun-try-side _ all dressed in white, _ that
la-zy fire, _ the fall ing snow, _ the mag-ic in __ the frost-y air, ___ that

Bb/C   F(add9)

feel-ing ev-'ry-where. It must have been _ the pret-ty lights _ that
cra-zy snow-ball fight. It could have been _ the stee-ple bell __ that
made me love you. On Christ-mas Eve _ a wish come true, _ that

Cm7   Bbmaj7   Gm7

glis-tened _ in the si-lent night, _ or may be just _ the stars so bright _ that
wrapped us ___ up with-in its spell. _ It on-ly took _ one kiss to know, _ it
night I ___ fell in love with you. _ It on-ly took _ one kiss to know, _ it

Bb/C   **To Coda** ⊕ | 1. Bbmaj7   Fmaj7

shined a-bove you. Our first Christ-mas,
must have been the
must have been the

Gm7   C9   Fmaj7   Bbm7   Eb9

more than _ we'd been dream-ing of. ___ Old Saint

Nich - 'las had his fin - gers crossed, that

we would fall in love. _ It mis - tle - toe.

Our first Christ - mas, more than _ we'd been dream - ing of. _

_____ Old Saint Nich - 'las

D.S. al Coda

must have known that kiss would lead to all of this. _ It

CODA

mis - tle - toe! It must have been the

mis - tle - toe! It must have been the

mis - tle - toe.

IT'S BEGINNING TO LOOK LIKE CHRISTMAS

By MEREDITH WILLSON

hop-a-long boots and a pis-tol that shoots is the wish of Bar-ney and Ben;

Dolls that will talk and will go for a walk is the hope of Jan-ice and Jen;   And

Mom and Dad can hard - ly wait for school to start a - gain. It's be -

JINGLE-BELL ROCK

Words and Music by JOE BEAL
and JIM BOOTHE

JINGLE BELLS

Words and Music by
J. PIERPONT

Dash - ing thru the snow, In a one - horse o - pen sleigh,
Bells on bob - tail ring, _____ Mak - ing spir - its bright, what

O'er the fields we go, Laugh - ing all the way.
fun it is to

ride and sing a sleigh - ing song to - night. Jin - gle bells,

Jin - gle bells, Jin - gle all the way! Oh, what fun it

is to ride in a one - horse o - pen sleigh! Oh,

one - horse o - pen sleigh.

JOLLY OLD ST. NICHOLAS

Traditional 19th Century American Carol

Jol - ly old Saint Nich - o - las, Lean your ear this way!
When the clock is strik - ing twelve, When I'm fast a - sleep,
John - ny wants a pair of skates; Su - sy wants a sled;

Don't you tell a sin - gle soul What I'm going to say;
Down the chim - ney broad and black, With your pack you'll creep;
Nel - lie wants a pic - ture book, Yel - low, blue and red;

Christ - mas Eve is com - ing soon; Now you dear old man,
All the stock - ings you will find Hang - ing in a row;
Now I think I'll leave to you What to give the rest;

Whis - per what you'll bring to me; Tell me if you can.
Mine will be the short - est one, You'll be sure to know.
Choose for me, dear San - ta Claus, You will know the best.

JOY TO THE WORLD

Words by ISAAC WATTS
Music by GEORGE FRIDERIC HANDEL
Arranged by LOWELL MASON

Brightly

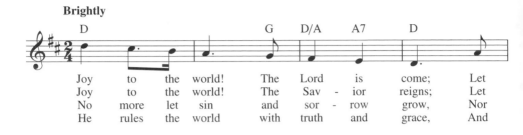

Joy to the world! The Lord is come; Let
Joy to the world! The Sav - ior reigns; Let
No more let sin and sor - row grow, Nor
He rules the world with truth and grace, And

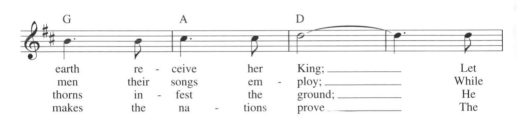

earth re - ceive her King; _____ Let
men their songs em - ploy; _____ While
thorns in - fest the ground; _____ He
makes the na - tions prove _____ The

ev - 'ry ___ heart ___ pre - pare _ Him _ room, ___ And
fields _ and _ floods, ___ rocks, hills _ and _ plains, ___ Re -
comes _ to ___ make ___ His bless - ings _ flow, ___ Far
glo - ries ___ of ___ His right - eous - ness, ___ And

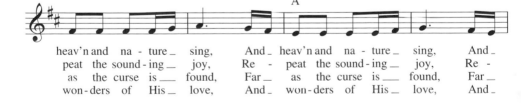

heav'n and na - ture _ sing, And _ heav'n and na - ture _ sing, And _
peat the sound - ing _ joy, Re - peat the sound - ing _ joy, Re -
as the curse is ___ found, Far _ as the curse is ___ found, Far _
won - ders of His _ love, And _ won - ders of His _ love, And _

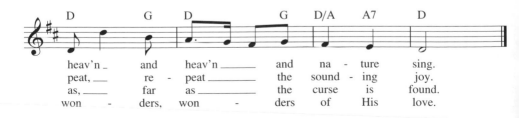

heav'n _ and heav'n _____ and na - ture sing.
peat, ___ re - peat _____ the sound - ing joy.
as, ___ far as _____ the curse is found.
won - ders, won - ders of His love.

LET IT SNOW! LET IT SNOW! LET IT SNOW!

Words by SAMMY CAHN
Music by JULE STYNE

LITTLE SAINT NICK

Words and Music by BRIAN WILSON
and MIKE LOVE

Moderately fast

Well, __ way up north where the air gets cold, __ there's a
lit - tle bob - sled, we call it Old Saint Nick, __ but she'll
haul- in' through the snow at a fright-'nin' speed __ with a

tale a - bout Christ-mas that you've all been told. __ And a
walk a to - bog - gan with a four - speed stick. _____ She's
half a doz-en deer __ with __ Ru - dy to lead. He's

real fa - mous cat all dressed up in red, __ and he
can - dy ap - ple red with a ski for a wheel, and when
got - ta wear his gog - gles 'cause the snow real - ly flies, and he's

spends the whole __ year work - in' out on his sled. __
San - ta hits the gas, man, just watch her __ peel. __   It's the
cruis - in' ev - 'ry pad with a lit - tle sur - prise. __

To Coda

Lit - tle Saint Nick. (Lit - tle Saint Nick.) __ It's the

1.
2.

Lit - tle Saint Nick. (Lit - tle Saint Nick.) __ Just a Saint Nick.)

Run, run, rein - deer. _____ Run, run, rein - deer.

Oh. _____ Run, run, rein - deer. _____

Run, run, rein - deer. He don't miss no one. And

CODA

Lit - tle Saint Nick. (Lit - tle Saint Nick.) Ah, _____

Mer - ry Christ - mas, Saint __ Nick. ____ Ah, _____
(Christ - mas comes this time each year.) _

A MARSHMALLOW WORLD

Words by CARL SIGMAN
Music by PETER DE ROSE

world is your snow - ball just for a song; get out and roll it a -

long. It's a yum - yum - my world made for sweet - hearts; ___ Take a

walk with your fa - vor - ite girl. It's a sug - ar date; _ what if spring is late? In

win - ter it's a marsh - mal - low world. ___ It's a world.

MERRY CHRISTMAS, DARLING

Words and Music by RICHARD CARPENTER
and FRANK POOLER

MISTER SANTA

Words and Music by
PAT BALLARD

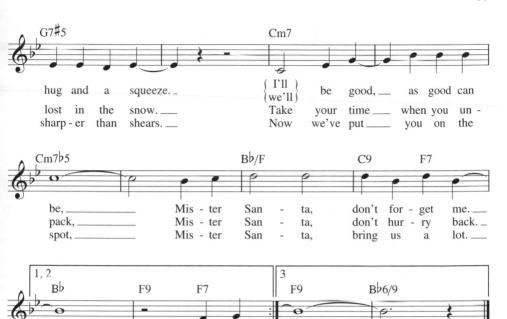

hug and a squeeze. ___ { I'll / we'll } be good, ___ as good can
lost in the snow. ___ Take your time ___ when you un -
sharp - er than shears. ___ Now we've put ___ you on the

be, _____ Mis - ter San - ta, don't for - get me. ___
pack, _____ Mis - ter San - ta, don't hur - ry back. ___
spot, _____ Mis - ter San - ta, bring us a lot. ___

1, 2
Bb   F9   F7

3
F9   Bb6/9

___ Mis - ter _____
___ Mis - ter

MISTLETOE AND HOLLY

Words and Music by FRANK SINATRA,
DOK STANFORD and HENRY W. SANICOLA

O CHRISTMAS TREE

Traditional German Carol

O Christ-mas tree! O Christ-mas tree, You stand in ver - dant beau - ty! O Christ - mas tree! O Christ - mas tree, You stand in ver - dant beau - ty! Your boughs are green in sum-mer's glow, And do not fade in win - ter's snow. O Christ-mas tree! O Christ-mas tree, You stand in ver - dant beau - ty!

THE MOST WONDERFUL TIME OF THE YEAR

Words and Music by EDDIE POLA
and GEORGE WYLE

Brightly, in one

It's the most won - der - ful time ____ of the
hap - hap - pi - est sea - son of
most won - der - ful time ____ of the

year, ____ with the kids jin - gle -
all, ____ with those hol - i - day
year. ____ There'll be much mis - tle -

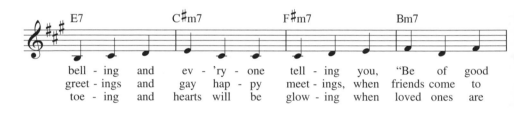

bell - ing and ev - 'ry - one tell - ing you, "Be of good
greet - ings and gay hap - py meet - ings, when friends come to
toe - ing and hearts will be glow - ing when loved ones are

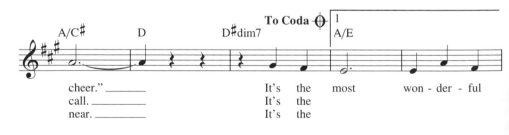

To Coda ⊕ | 1

cheer." ____ It's the most won - der - ful
call. ____ It's the
near. ____ It's the

time ____ of the year. ____

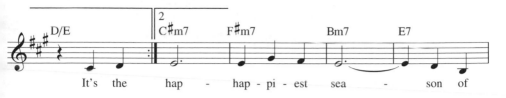

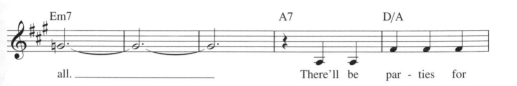

It's the hap - hap - pi - est sea - son of

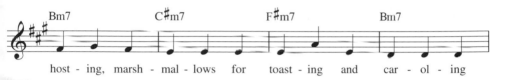

all. _____ There'll be par - ties for

host - ing, marsh - mal - lows for toast - ing and car - ol - ing

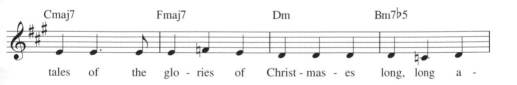

out in the snow. There'll be scar - y ghost sto - ries and

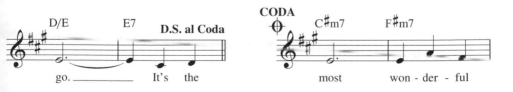

tales of the glo - ries of Christ - mas - es long, long a -

go. _____ It's the   most won - der - ful

time _____ of the year. _____

MY FAVORITE THINGS
from THE SOUND OF MUSIC

Lyrics by OSCAR HAMMERSTEIN II
Music by RICHARD RODGERS

O COME, ALL YE FAITHFUL
(Adeste Fideles)
Words and Music by JOHN FRANCIS WADE
translated by Frederick Oakley

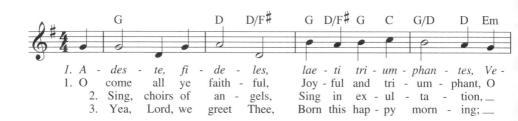

1. A - des - te, fi - de - les, lae - ti tri - um - phan - tes, Ve -
1. O come all ye faith - ful, Joy - ful and tri - um - phant, O
2. Sing, choirs of an - gels, Sing in ex - ul - ta - tion, ___
3. Yea, Lord, we greet Thee, Born this hap - py morn - ing; ___

ni - te, ve - ni - te in Beth - le - hem.
come ye, O come ye to Beth - le - hem;
Sing all ye cit - i - zens of heav'n ___ a - bove.
Je - sus, to Thee ___ be all glo - ry giv'n.

Na - tum vi - de - te Re - gem an - ge - lor - um. Ve -
Come and be - hold Him, Born the King of an - gels;
Glo - ry to God ___ In ___ the ___ high - est. } O
Word of the Fa - ther, Now in flesh ap - pear - ing:)

ni - te a - do - re - mus, ve - ni - te a - do - re - mus, ve -
come let us a - dore Him, O come let us a - dore Him, O

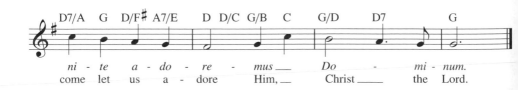

ni - te a - do - re - mus ___ Do - mi - num.
come let us a - dore Him, ___ Christ ___ the Lord.

O HOLY NIGHT

French Words by PLACIDE CAPPEAU
English Words by JOHN S. DWIGHT
Music by ADOLPHE ADAM

O LITTLE TOWN OF BETHLEHEM

Words by PHILLIPS BROOKS
Music by LEWIS H. REDNER

SANTA CLAUS IS COMIN' TO TOWN

Words by HAVEN GILLESPIE
Music by J. FRED COOTS

ROCKIN' AROUND THE CHRISTMAS TREE

Music and Lyrics by
JOHNNY MARKS

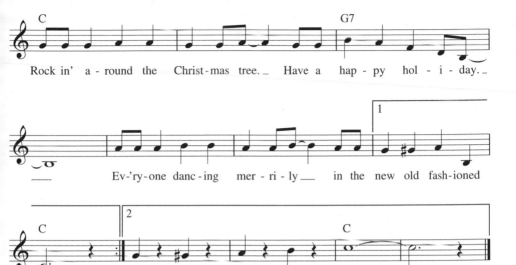

Rock in' a - round the Christ-mas tree. _ Have a hap - py hol - i - day. _

_ Ev-'ry-one danc - ing mer - ri - ly _ in the new old fash-ioned

way.   new   old   fash - ioned   way. _____

RUDOLPH THE RED-NOSED REINDEER

Music and Lyrics by
JOHNNY MARKS

C   C#dim7   G/D   Gmaj7   G#dim7   Am7   D7

say,   "Ru - dolph, with your nose so bright,   won't you guide my

G7   C

sleigh   to - night?" _   Then how   the rein - deer   loved him

                  F#dim7 G7

as they shout - ed out with   glee: "Ru - dolph the red - nosed rein - deer,

      C#dim7   G7   C

you'll go down in   his - to - ry!" _____

SHAKE ME I RATTLE
(Squeeze Me I Cry)
Words and Music by HAL HACKADY
and CHARLES NAYLOR

Moderately slow

I was pass - ing by a toy shop on the cor - ner of the
called an - oth - er toy shop on a square so long a -
late and snow was fall - ing as the shop - pers hur - ried

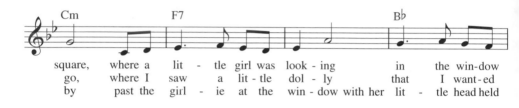

square, where a lit - tle girl was look - ing in the win-dow
go, where I saw a lit - tle dol - ly that I want-ed
by past the girl - ie at the win - dow with her lit - tle head held

there. She was look - ing at a dol - ly in a dress of ros - y
so. I re - mem - bered, I re - mem-bered how I longed to make it
high. They were clos - ing up the toy shop as I hur - ried thru the

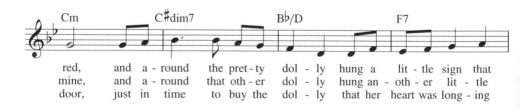

red, and a - round the pret - ty dol - ly hung a lit - tle sign that
mine, and a - round that oth - er dol - ly hung an - oth - er lit - tle
door, just in time to buy the dol - ly that her heart was long - ing

said:
sign:
for.

Shake me, I rat - tle. Squeeze me, I

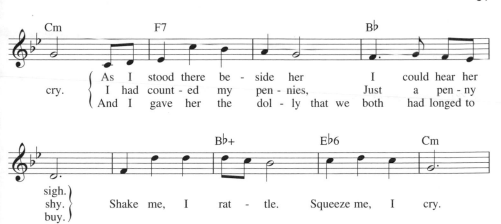

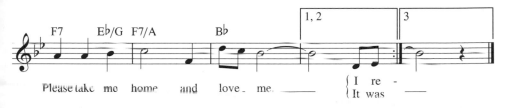

SILENT NIGHT

Words by JOSEPH MOHR
Translated by JOHN F. YOUNG
Music by FRANZ X. GRUBER

SILVER BELLS

from the Paramount Picture THE LEMON DROP KID
Words and Music by JAY LIVINGSTON
and RAY EVANS

SOMEWHERE IN MY MEMORY

from the Twentieth Century Fox Motion Picture HOME ALONE
Words by LESLIE BRICUSSE
Music by JOHN WILLIAMS

THIS CHRISTMAS

Words and Music by DONNY HATHAWAY
and NADINE McKINNOR

TOYLAND

from BABES IN TOYLAND

Words by GLEN MacDONOUGH
Music by VICTOR HERBERT

Toy - land! Toy - land! Lit - tle girl and boy - land.
Child - hood's joy - land, mys - tic mer - ry Toy - land!

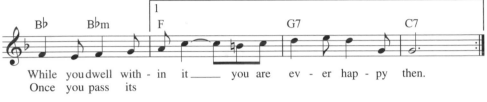

While you dwell with - in it ____ you are ev - er hap - py then.
Once you pass its

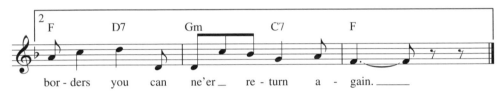

bor - ders you can ne'er _ re - turn a - gain. _____

UP ON THE HOUSETOP

Words and Music by
B.R. HANDY

THE TWELVE DAYS OF CHRISTMAS

Traditional English Carol

7. On the seventh day of Christmas my true love gave to me:
   Seven swans a-swimming,...

8. ...Eight maids a-milking,...

9. ...Nine ladies dancing,...

10. ...Ten lords a-leaping,...

11. ...'Leven pipers piping,...

12. ...Twelve drummers drumming,...

WE THREE KINGS OF ORIENT ARE

Words and Music by
JOHN H. HOPKINS, JR.

WE WISH YOU A MERRY CHRISTMAS

Traditional English Folksong

We wish you a mer-ry Christ-mas, we wish you a mer-ry

Christ-mas, we wish you a mer-ry Christ-mas, And a hap-py New

Year! Good tid-ings to you, wher-ev-er you are; Good

tid-ings for Christ-mas, And a hap-py New Year!

WHAT ARE YOU DOING NEW YEAR'S EVE?

By FRANK LOESSER

WONDERFUL CHRISTMASTIME

Words and Music by
PAUL McCARTNEY

YOU'RE ALL I WANT FOR CHRISTMAS

Words and Music by GLEN MOORE
and SEGER ELLIS